OOR WULLIE

A' Creatures Great an' Small

It was not long after the dawn of DC Thomson's Fun Section in The Sunday Post that The Broons and Oor Wullie had their first encounters with some colourful creatures. The harassed humans soon learnt however that not all of them were bright and beautiful, nor very wise and wonderful...

And so, for all animal lovers, this collection features farmyard fauna (full of clumsy cuddies and not so cuddly coos), Scotland's famous wildlife, and man's best friend — their beloved and debatably domesticated pets. Of course, the most famous of these are Oor Wullie's own Jeemie the Moose, who was not long to follow his owner in the comic pages, and the newer but equally-loved addition of Wee Harry, Wullie's wily Westie! Both can be seen horsing around among these pages of classic Broons and Oor Wullie strips, Wee Harry's own comic, and even an exclusive story starring the dynamic duo on their own adventure across Scotland!

Well, what are you waiting for? Shake a tail feather and get reading!

© DCT Consumer Products (UK) Ltd. 2021
D.C. Thomson and Co. Ltd.,
185 Fleet Street,
London EC4A 2HS.

Printed in the EU.

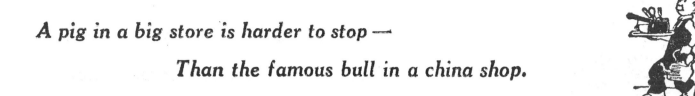

A pig in a big store is harder to stop —

Than the famous bull in a china shop.

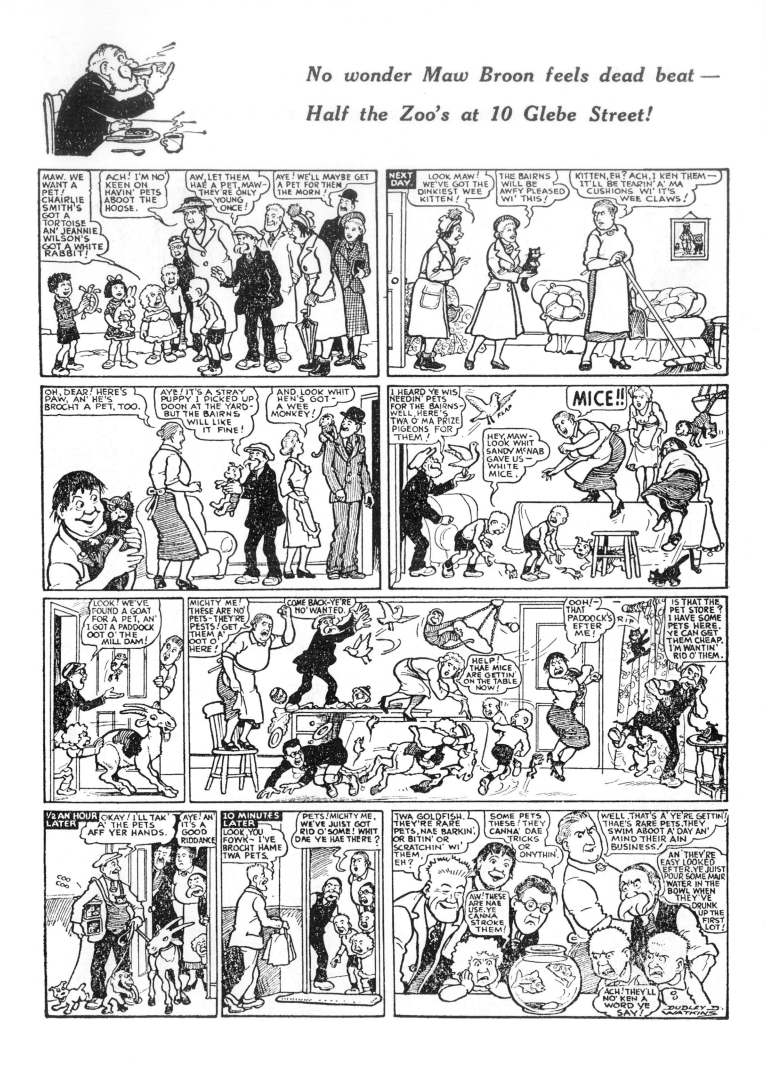

No wonder Maw Broon feels dead beat —
Half the Zoo's at 10 Glebe Street!

He's loupin' dykes and jumpin' hedges —
Because he pinched his mither's vegs.

GOWNS

Gran'paw's not the one to shirk —

An easy job of " donkey-work " !

Wullie's bonny budgie's dumb—

And that's sure lucky for his chum!

Gran'paw's looking awfy glum —

He thought that animals were DUMB !

Oor Wullie's fancy dress looks great —

Alas! he's just a day ower late.

The Broons find only one way out—
When tired of sausage. Do without!

Here's a trick that's mighty fine —

For flying fish, a flying line.

They always say that a laddie's best pal is his dug — and Wee Harry proves no exception! After his introduction as Wullie's canine companion, the wild Westie moved on to occupy his own corner of the fun pages, sharing a pup's perspective on the often farcical human world. But don't be fooled by his cute, fluffy exterior. Behind the fuzz is a mind worthy of Mensa — at least when it comes to getting his own way!

Along with his best pal, Jock, Harry's hijinks often rival his owners', as he schemes his way to sausages, displays talents for treats, hangs out with other hounds and chases down chortles from Sunday Post readers of all ages. Fresh but familiar, each mini-strip captures what it means to be — or own — a dog in Scotland.

There's many a hoof —

'Twixt the floor and the roof.

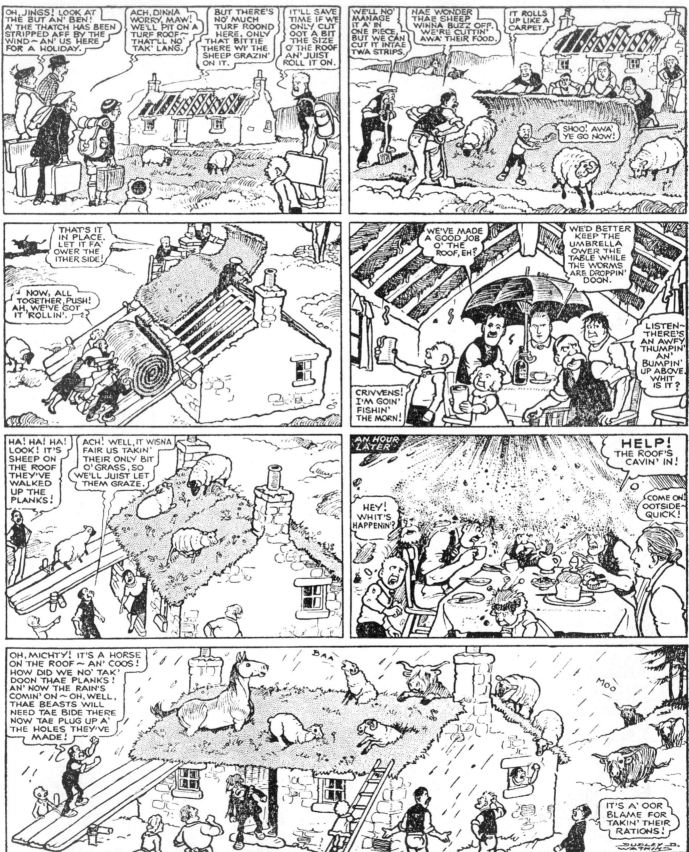

It's a dog's life Wullie's found —

Deliverin' papers on his round.

There's pandemonium in the hoose —

A coo-sized dog is on the loose.

Oor Wullie gets an education —

At the School of Equitation.

The coos seem tae ken —

Far mair than the men!

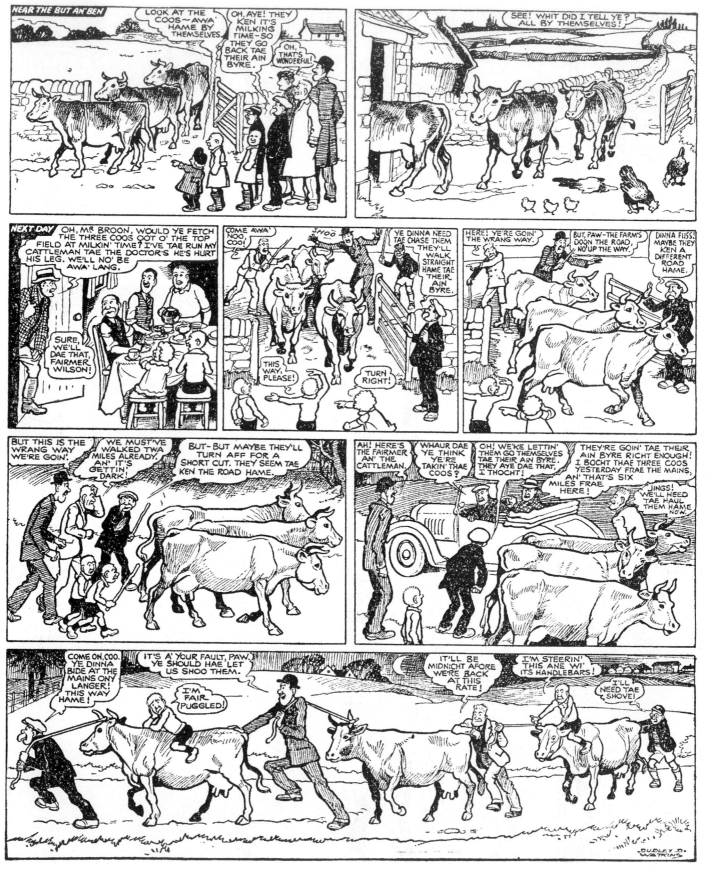

There's ae thing, Wull, ye're awfu' plucky —

Some farmyard jobs can be fell mucky.

Gran'paw was a poor sick body—

Till he saw the hungry cuddy!

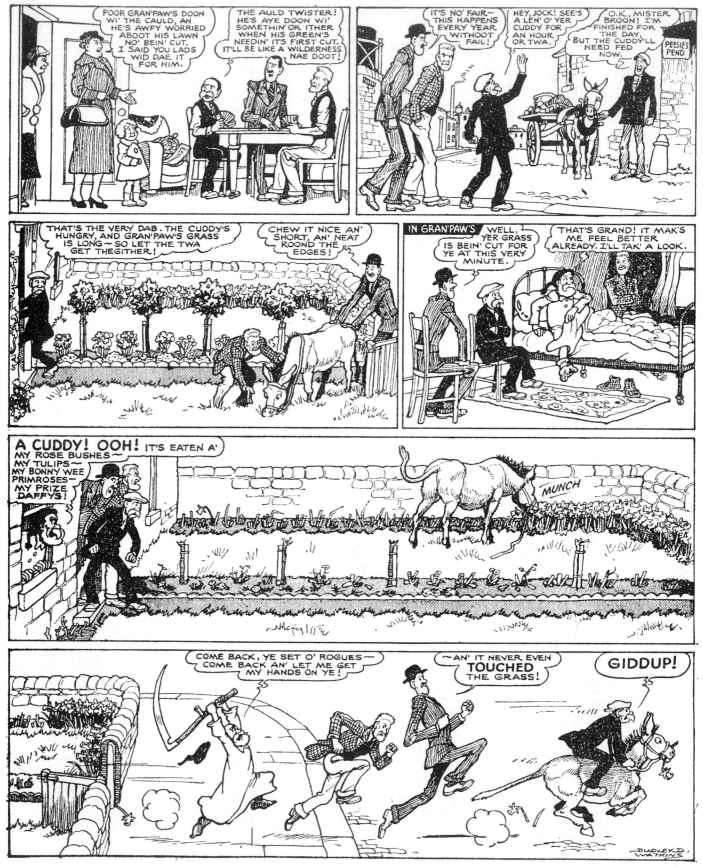

It fairly hits up miles per hour —

Oor Wullie's car is one-DOG-power.

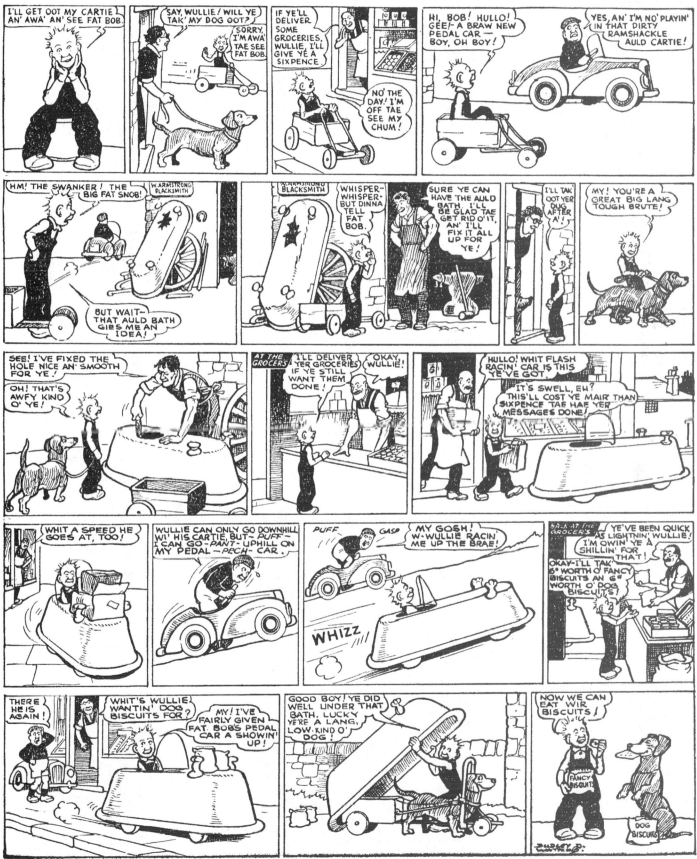

Look at the lads. Their heads are hung—

They're no' so smart. They've a' been stung!

Oor Wullie's cheap biscuits must have a queer taste —
He tries to be kind, but he keeps gettin' chased.

The cause of a Glebe Street hullaballoo —

Paw's tonic an' the tale o' a coo!

With rage, hear Gran'paw hoot—

The family's let his lodger oot!

Cats can cause a lot o' strife—

They lead Wullie a real dog's life!

See what Paw an' Gran'paw caught —

But it's a secret who caught what!

Birds that moo, an' sheep that quack —

Nae wonder the farmer's ta'en aback!

The bus has plenty seats to suit—

but the Broons prefer to ride on foot!

Wullie hasn't got a clue —

When it comes to working in the zoo.

Granpaw's fly! Trust him to find—

A 'judge' who isn't colour blind!

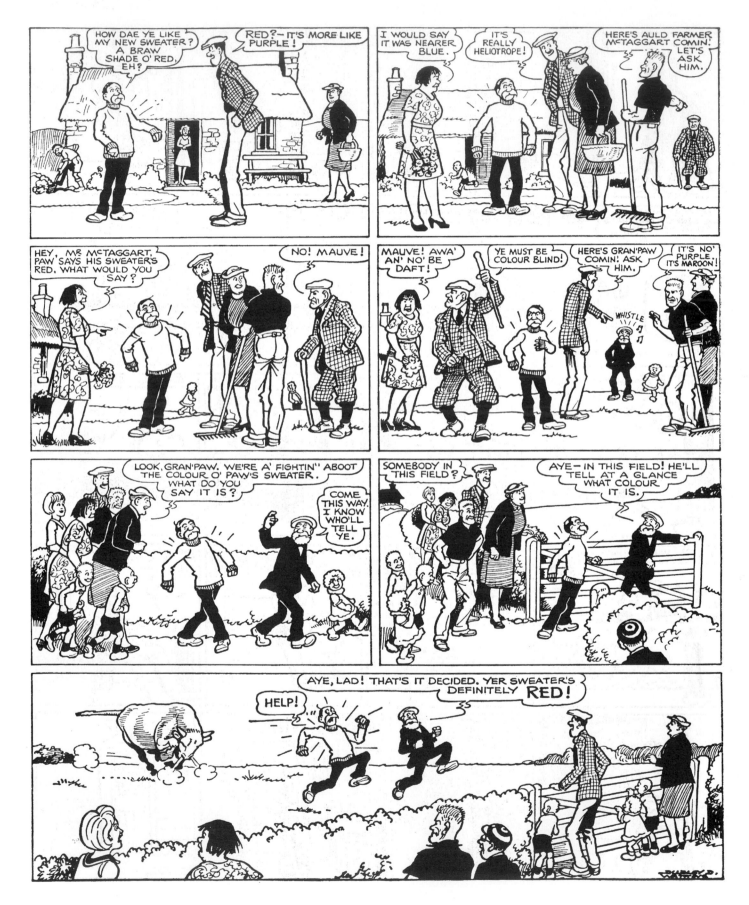

Barber Wullie ends up yelping—

His scalping's in need of helping!

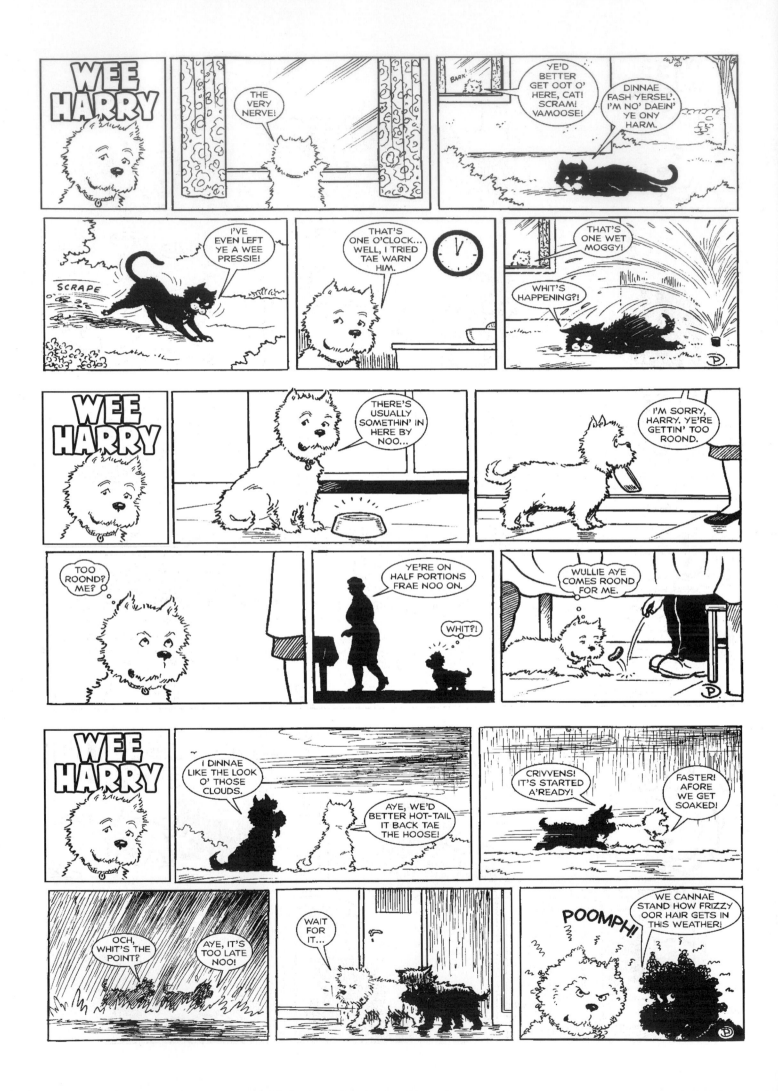

Oil drum, coal sack, cardboard box—

The Broons new 'clothes' give folk big shocks!

Cats and dogs, a crab, a moose —

There's lots o' fun when they get loose.

A tweet-tweet here, a quack-quack there—
No wonder Gran'paw's in despair!

Wullie kens the very place —

To land his cousin in disgrace!

Even Wullie canna thole—

An extra pupil on the 'roll'!

Paw acts tough with this wee pup—

But then, guess who it butters up!

Oor Wullie's fed up repeatin'—
Cricket bats are not for eatin'!

That wee beastie winna hurt—

In fact, it's just a little squirt!

The 'sheriff' has a job to do—

He hears that thieves have pinched a coo!

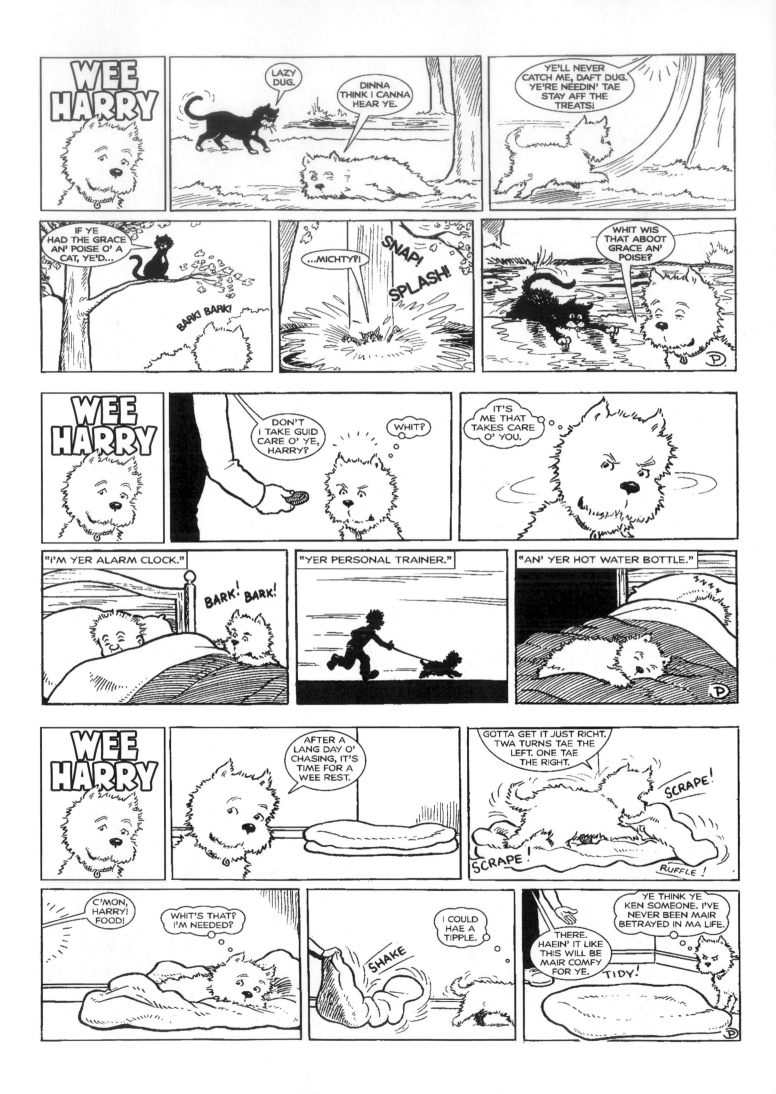

Lads wi' beards, that's what they're after—

But when they meet one, oh, the laughter!

One apple left upon that tree—

And who will get it? Wait and see!

Bairns like milk, that's true enough—
But this wee one drinks pints o' the stuff!

Wull finds a worm, as you'll see—

Not underground—but up a tree!

Parp! Honk! Hoot! Oor Wullie's fated—
To have his tooter confiscated!

Wullie beats the pests in time—

But it's a proper pantomime!

For " peat's " sake—

What a mistake!

This patchy time for Maw—

Is soon ' enjoyed ' by one an a'!

Carpet cleaning can be fun—

See how Wullie gets it done!

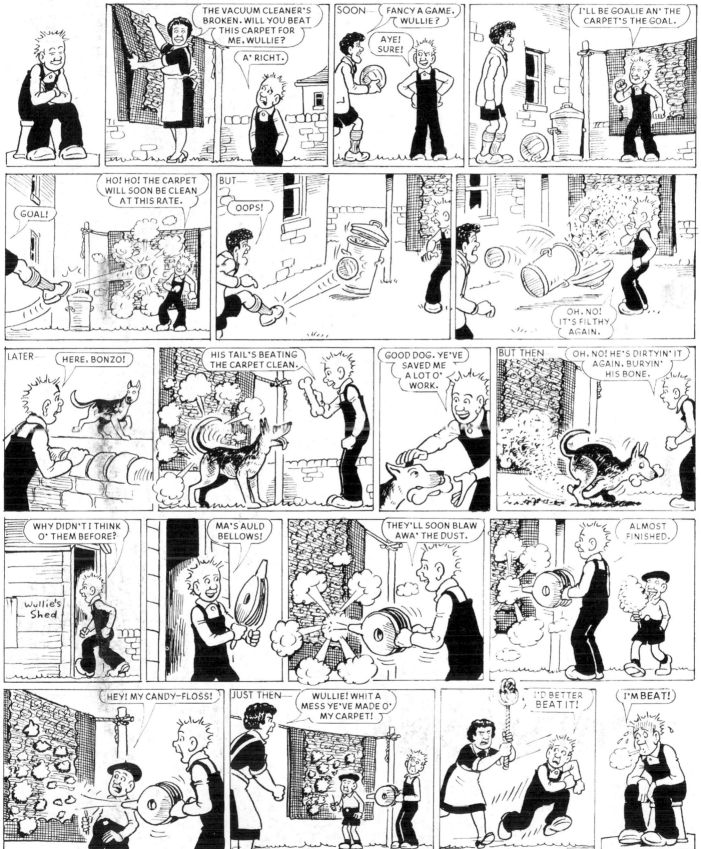

Hen and Joe get a fright—

From a very ' fishy ' sight!

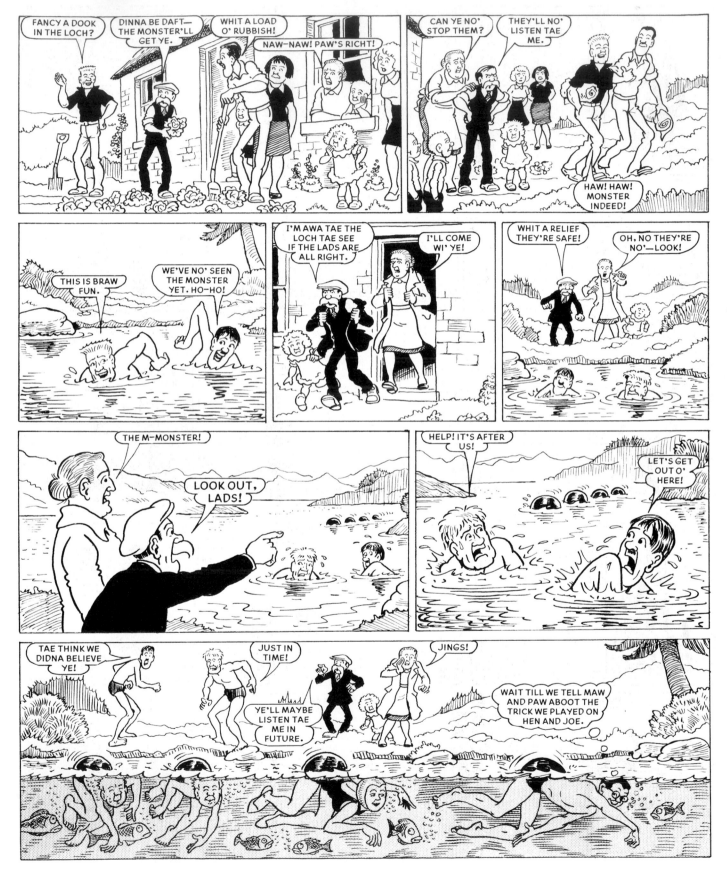

Wullie sure feels " sheepish " when—

Aunty Jean sees him again!

Help m'boab! It's no' half funny—

When Daphne turns into a bunny!

This sleepy heid—

Is smart indeed!

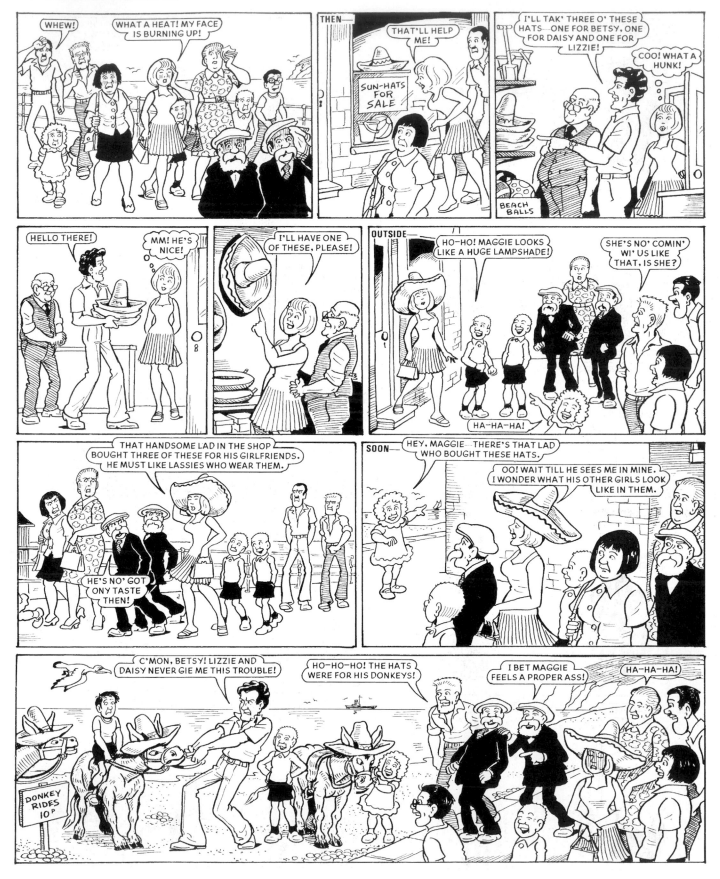

Oor laddie finds he's strength enough—
To move a train with just one puff!

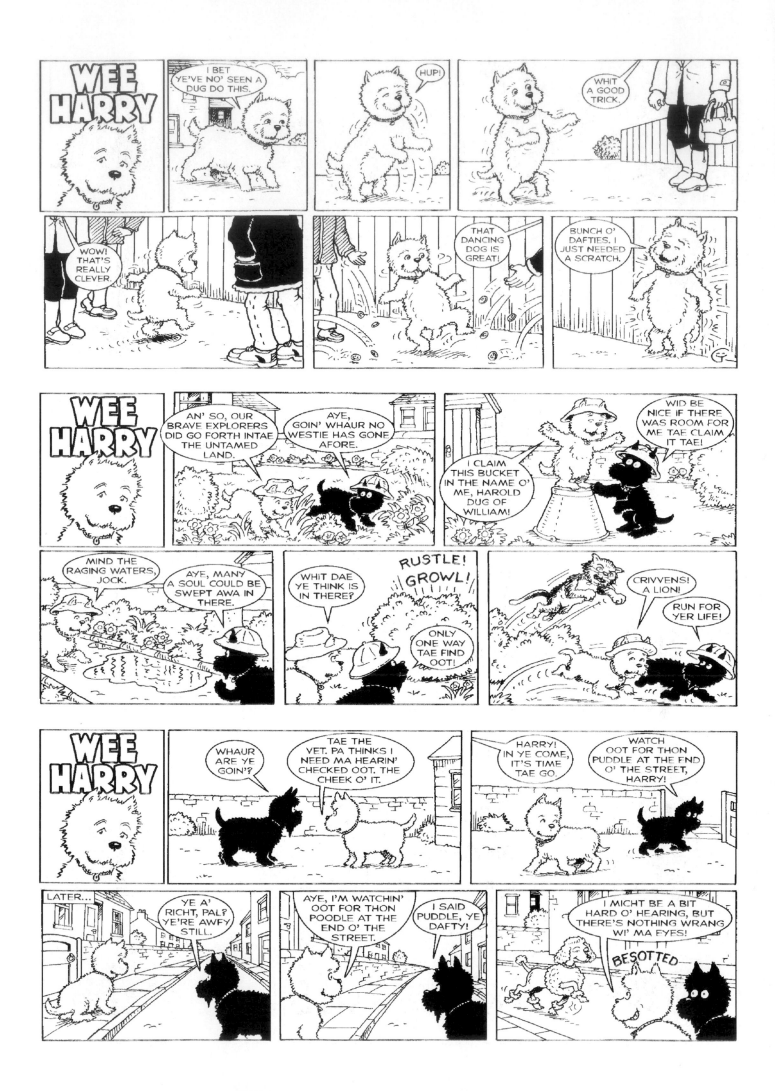

This horseplay by Paw—

Means a " run-in " wi' the Law!

This birthday gift's so hard to choose—

The enorMOUSE task gives Wull the blues!

It's a dog's life, they find—

When they try tae be kind!

...but a wee moose's life—

Is full o' strife!

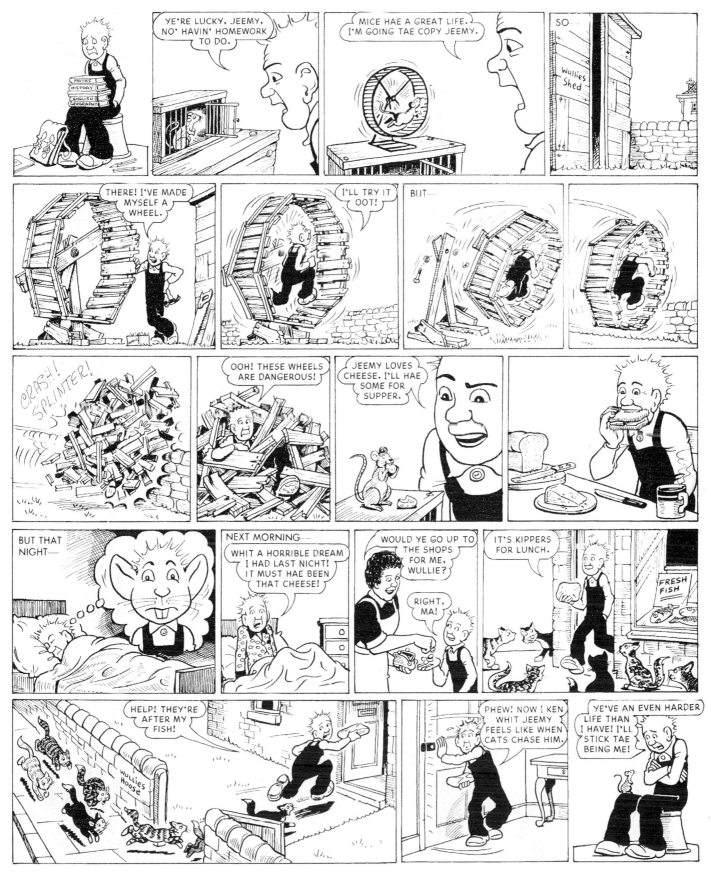

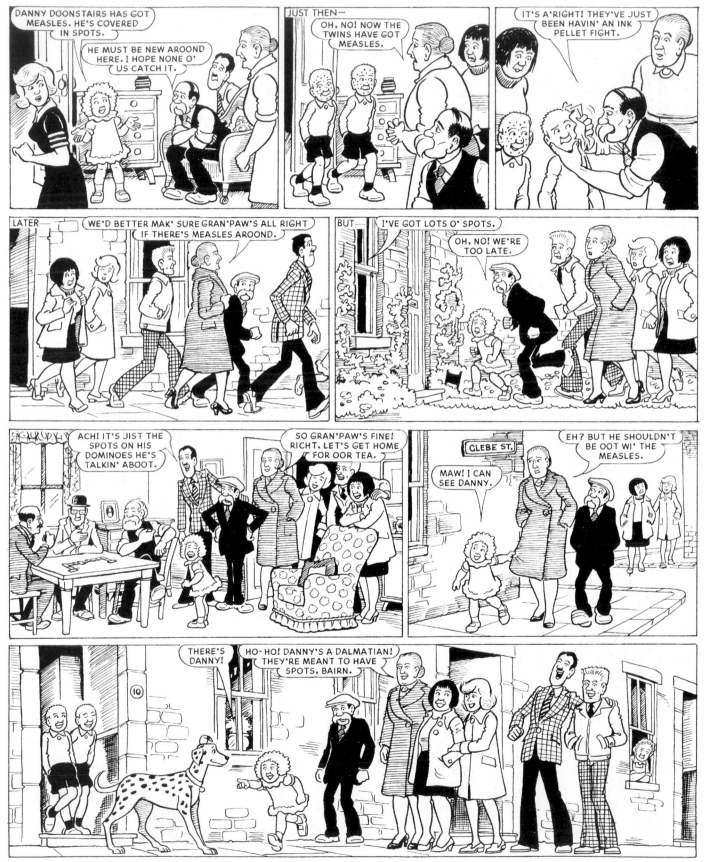

This hat's a handy thing indeed—

It's everywhere, 'cept on his heid!

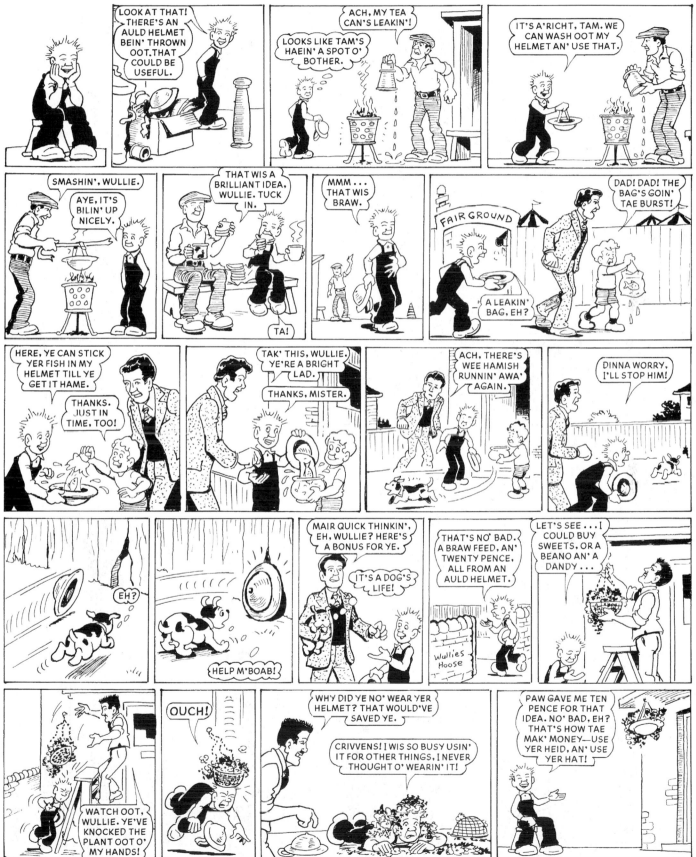

It's a sad, sad day for Gran'paw Broon—

When he gets a seat, he CAN'T sit doon!

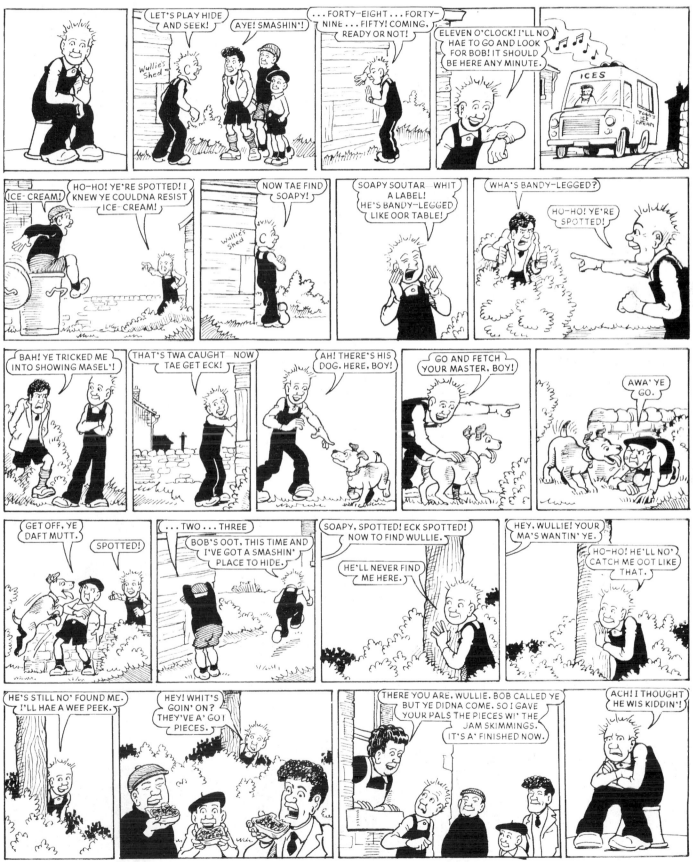

Oor lad feels richt silly —

They'll be ca'in him Pussycat Wullie!

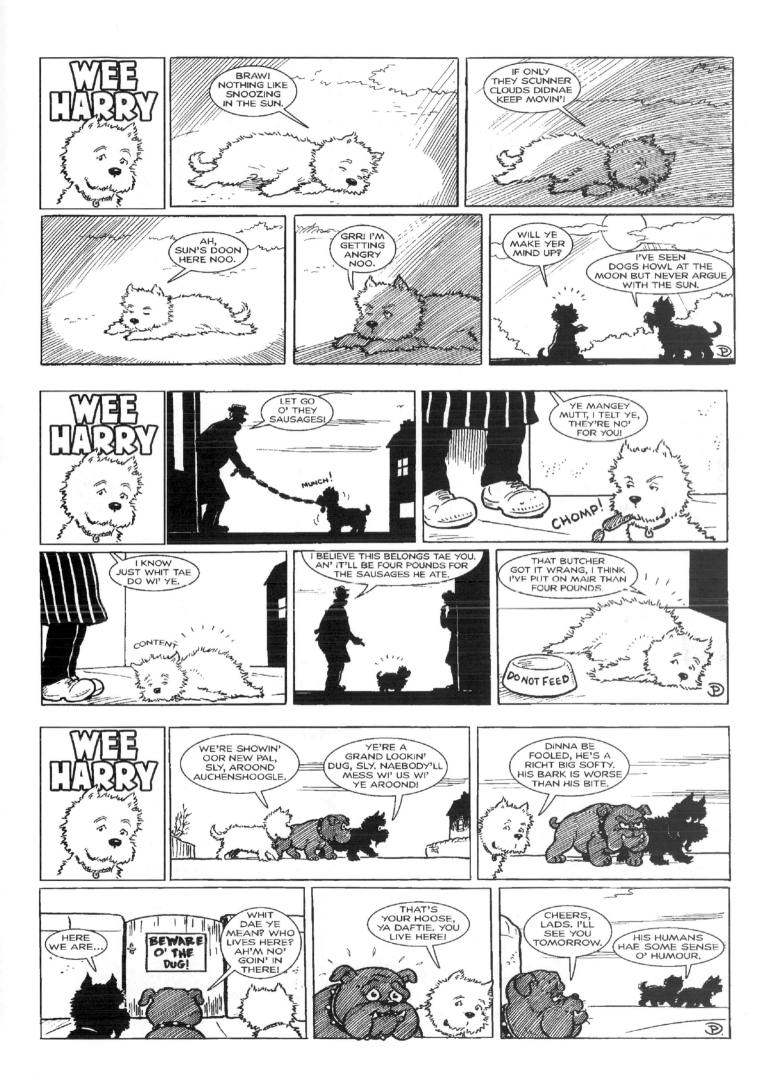

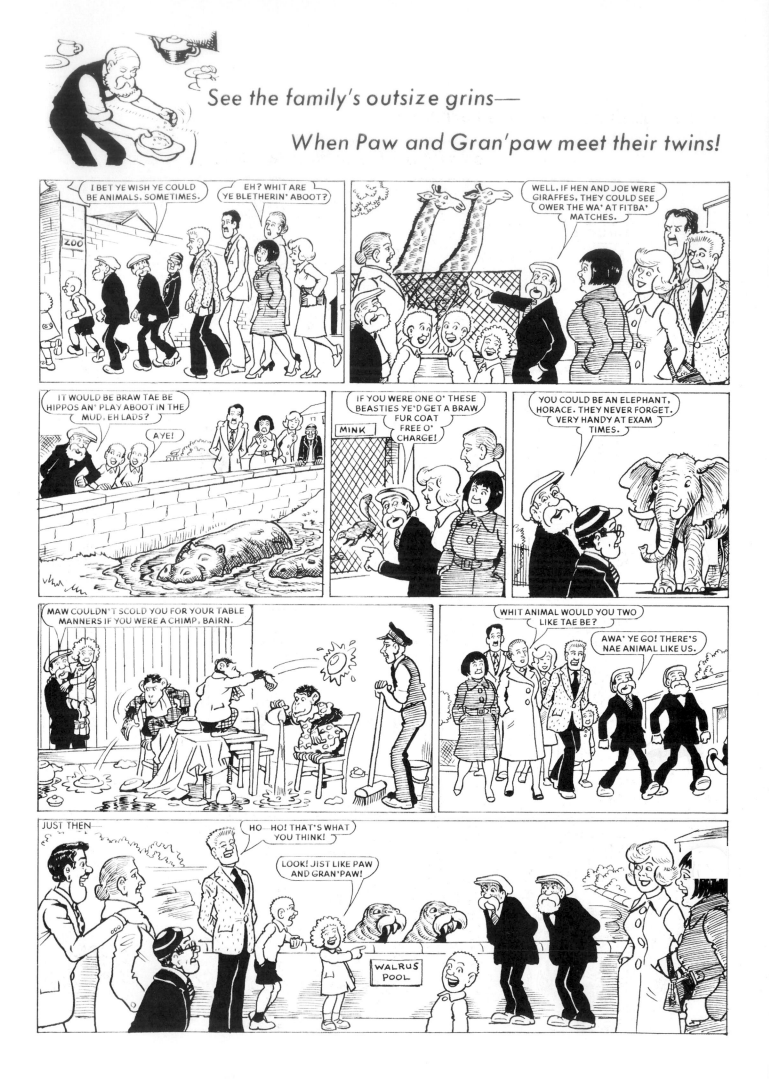

See the family's outsize grins—

When Paw and Gran'paw meet their twins!

Wullie's pals soon mak' an error —

stirrin' up the tartan terror!

Primrose nearly has a fit

when Wullie says "she pongs a bit"!

They dinna half fret—

Aboot Billy Greene's pet!

A dog exchange scheme

ends as love's dog dream!

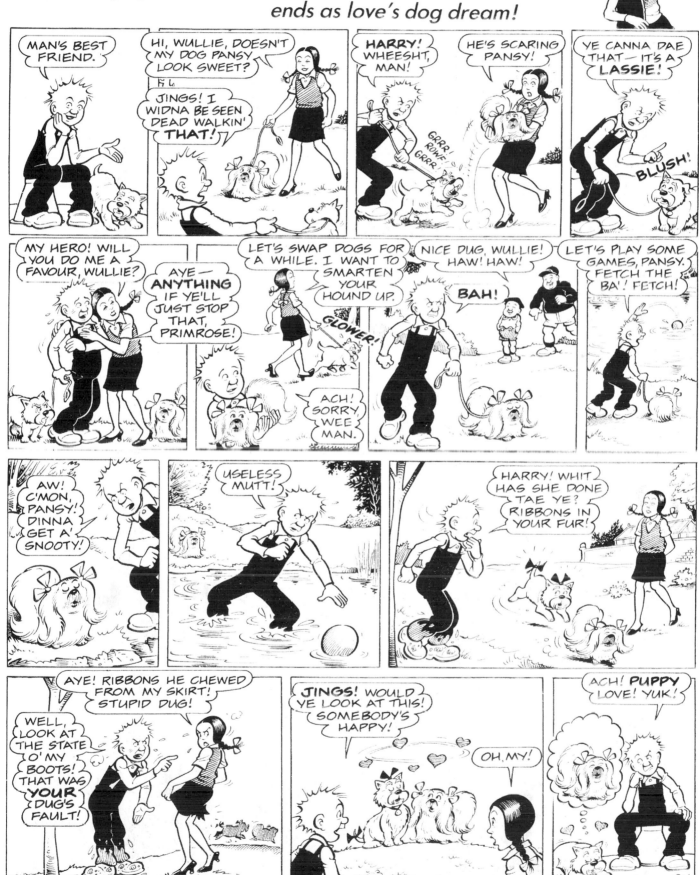

The bairn doesnae like tae see —

— a pussycat stuck up a tree.

Wash this beastie doon the plug . . .

. . . or try tae help oot the little bug?

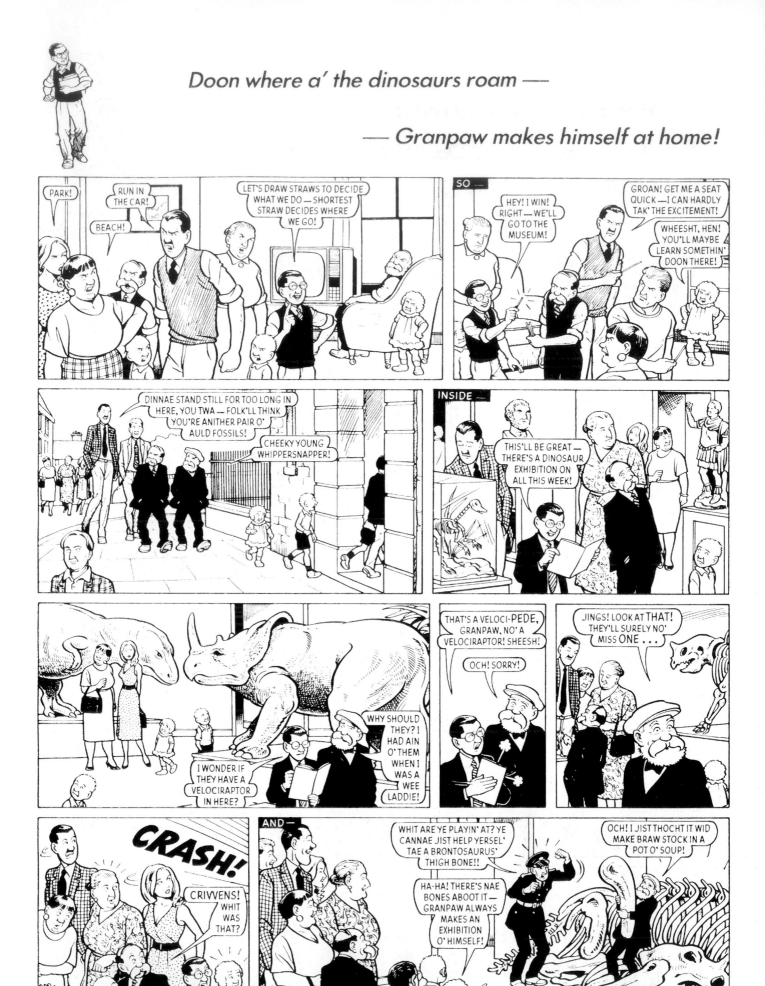

Harry, the dog, tak's every chance . . .

. . . to lead Oor Wullie a merry dance!

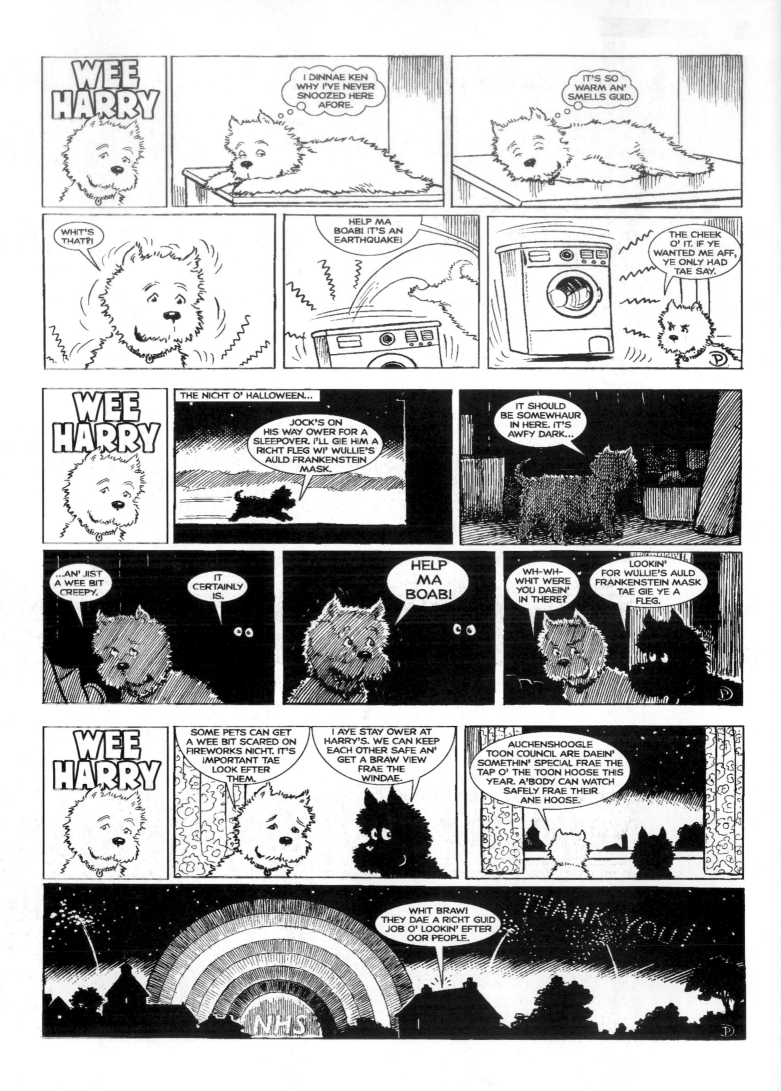

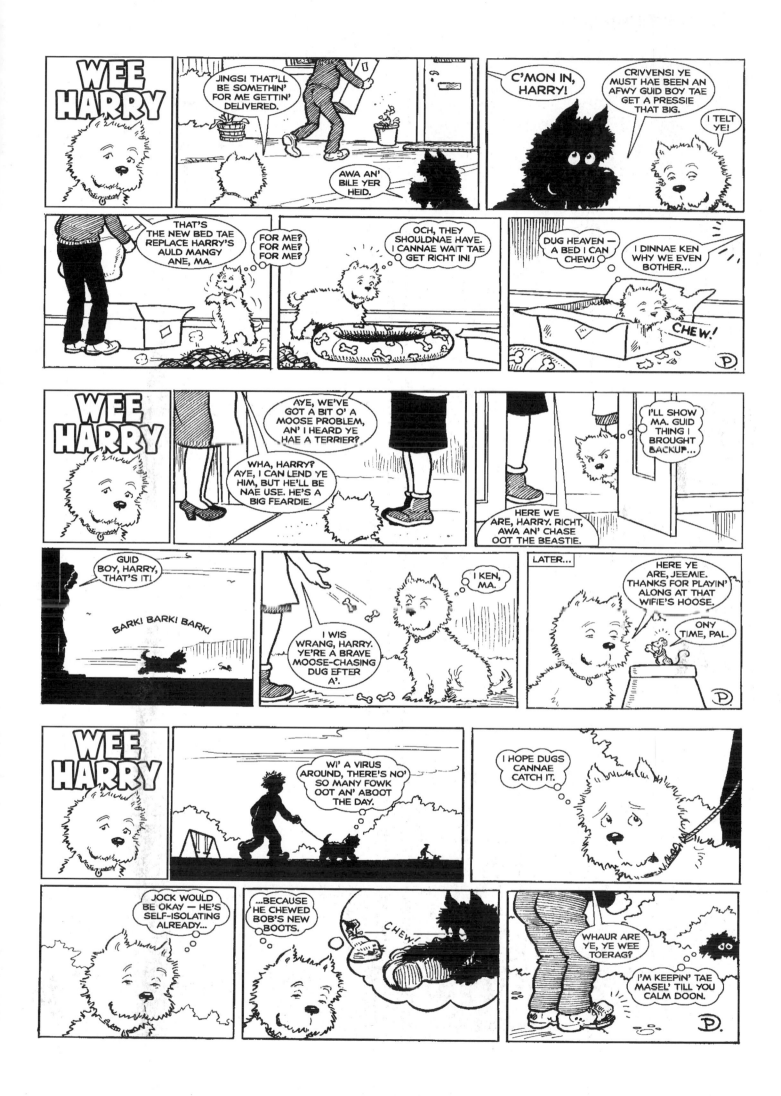

It's the laddies' yearly climb.

But wha'll mak' it in the quickest time?

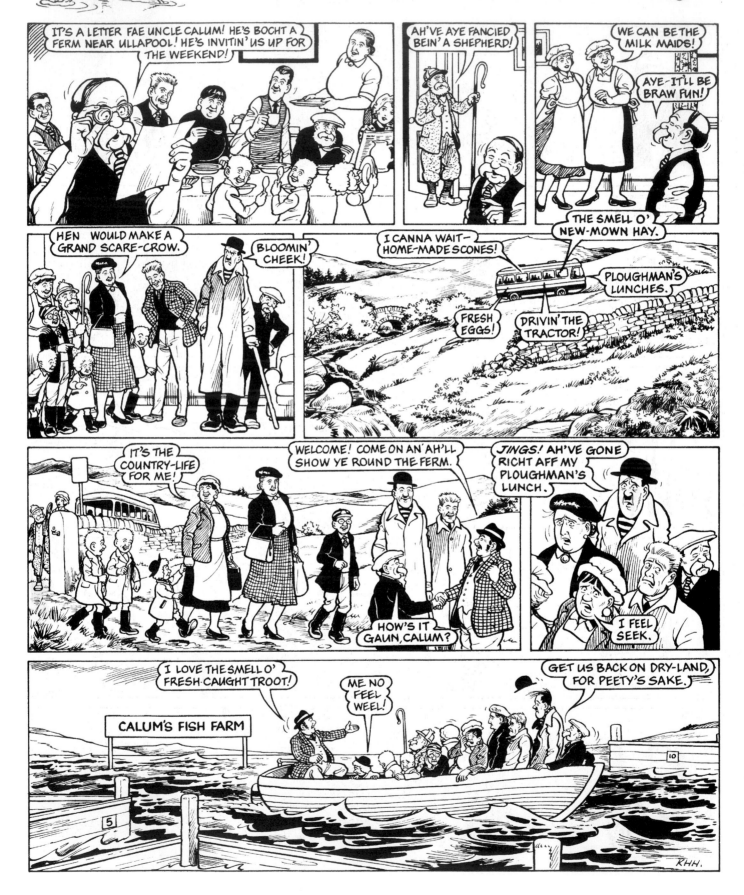

What's this we've got here . . .

. . . Wullie in cowboy gear?

They're fed up to the back teeth —

— o' this lad from Cowdenbeath.

Jeemy's new accommodation . . .

. . . causes Wullie much frustration.

Ye can bet Paw's gonnae be wishing —

— he'd been mair fly aboot fly-fishing.

This guid turn is bound tae be . . .

. . . another big cat-astrophe.

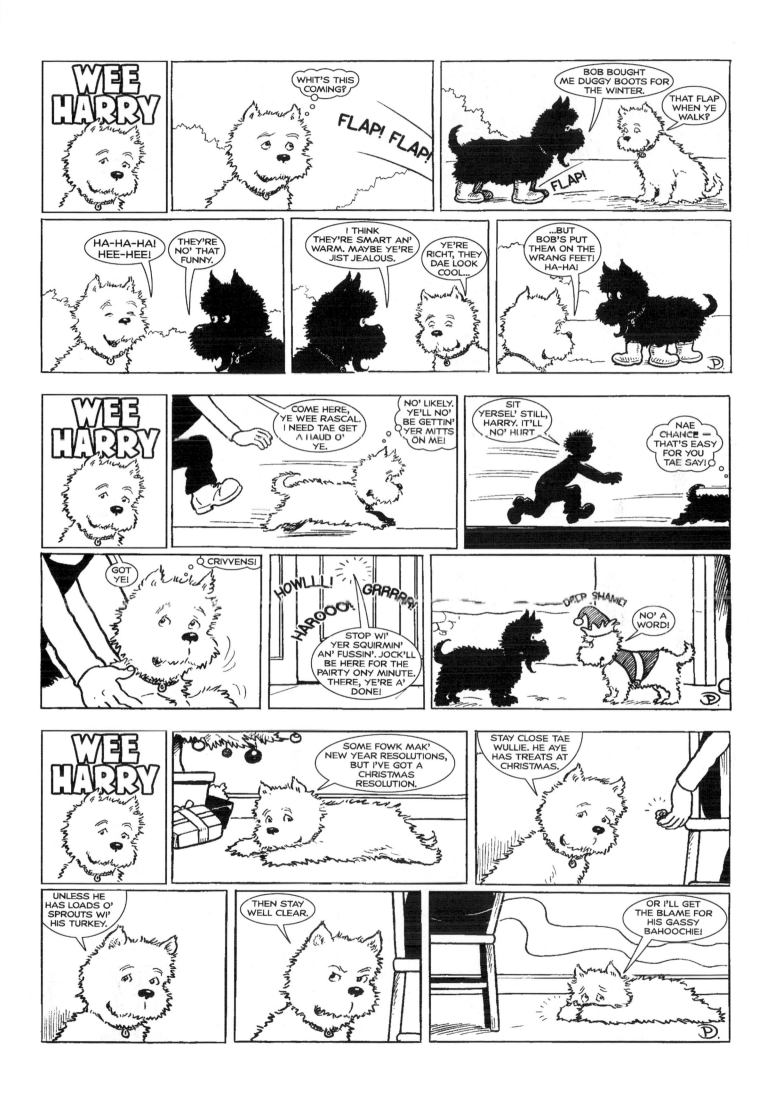

Fish for a', they think but, "Och!"

There's strict new rules doon at the loch.

Wullie dreams o' landin' a whopper . . .

. . . but, very soon, he comes a cropper!

How will Paw awake his flock —
— withoot his trusty alarm clock?

When it comes tae navigation . . .

. . . Wullie's team's a revelation!

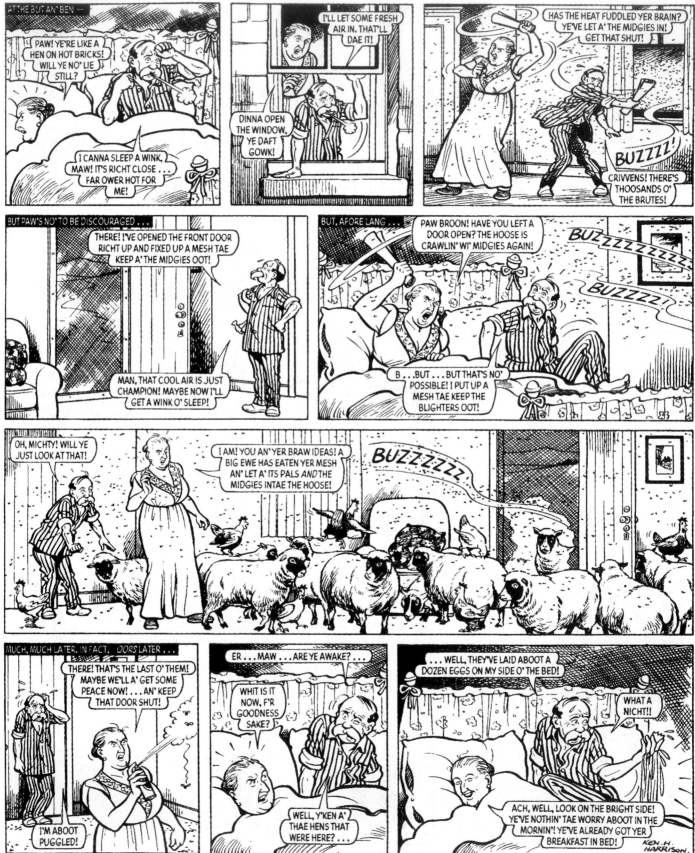

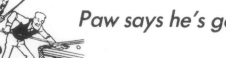

Paw says he's goin' tae cut the grass —

but does he know what'll come to pass?

If he hadnae messed aboot on the way . . .

. . . there'd be nae need tae see Farmer Gray.

What worries them a' . . .

. . . is they micht look like Paw!

KHH.

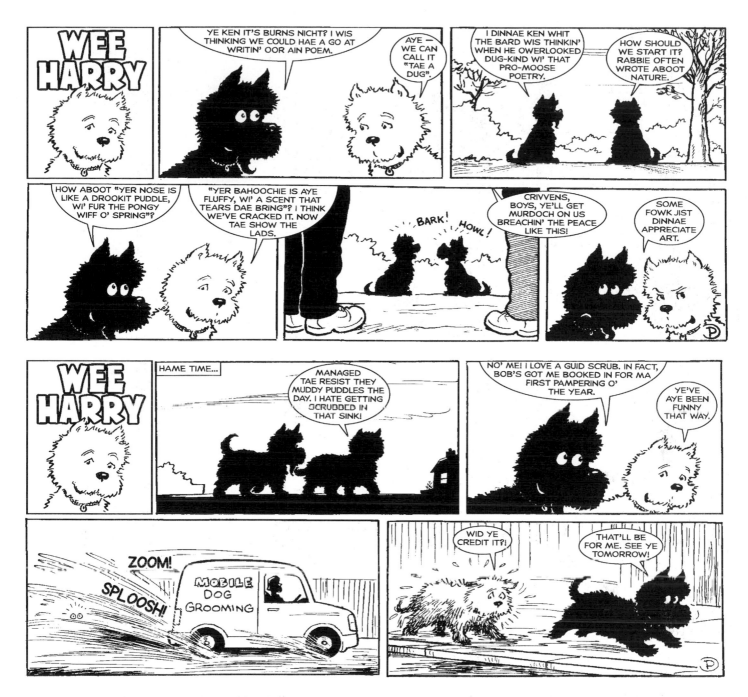

That's not quite all, folks! We hope you've enjoyed our selection of Wee Harry mini-strips and remember you can catch him every week in the pages of The Sunday Post. There's also an exclusive, never before printed Wee Harry adventure story later in this book. Join Jeemie, Jock and Harry as they make their way across Scotland, taking the lang way roond! But, before that here's another section of classic Oor Wullie and The Broons some of which Wee Harry co-stars in.

Time tae clean oot his pet's hooses . . .

. . . Harry, the dog's, an' Jeemy, the moose's!

This cat's dearest wish . . .

. . . is tae pinch Bob's fish.

Paw Broon wants tae get some space . . .

. . . but he's aboot to lose some face!

Nae wonder Wullie's face is trippin'.

These new boots are really nippin'!

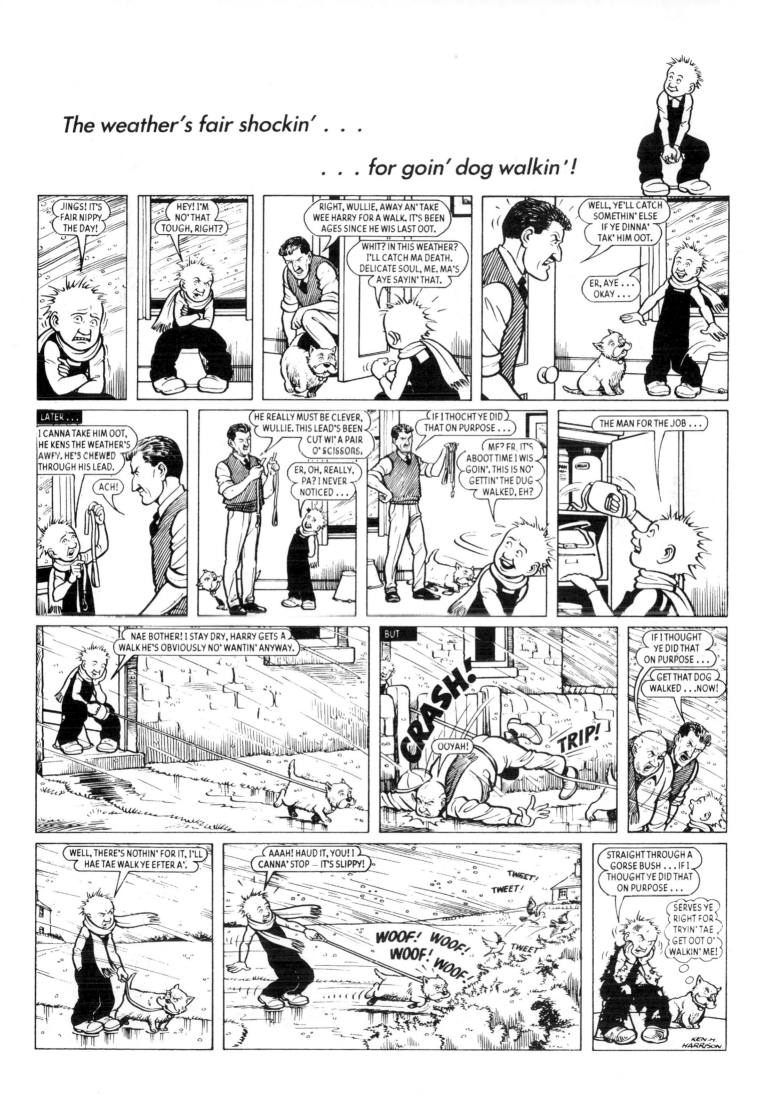

Oor hero goes the whole hog . . .

. . . tryin' tae train his dog.

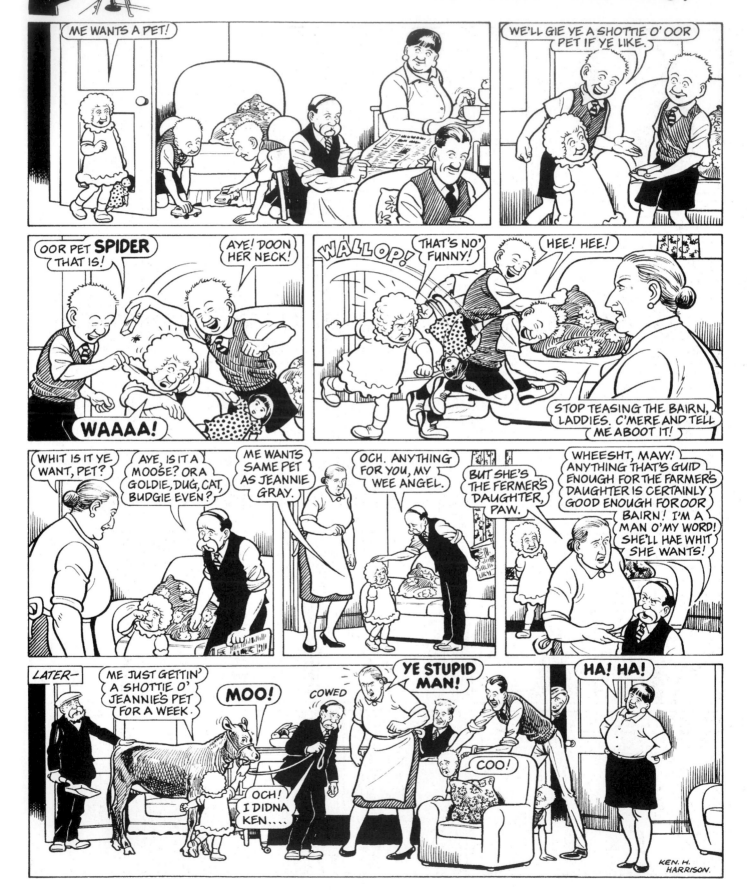

Afore we get tae an all-new adventure,
A trip that turns oot tae be a risky venture.
Here's a classic find in a book frae 1953,
But wha dae ye think this could be?
It's a pet moose whit Wullie cries Teenie,
Perhaps a distant relative o' a certain Wee Jeemie...

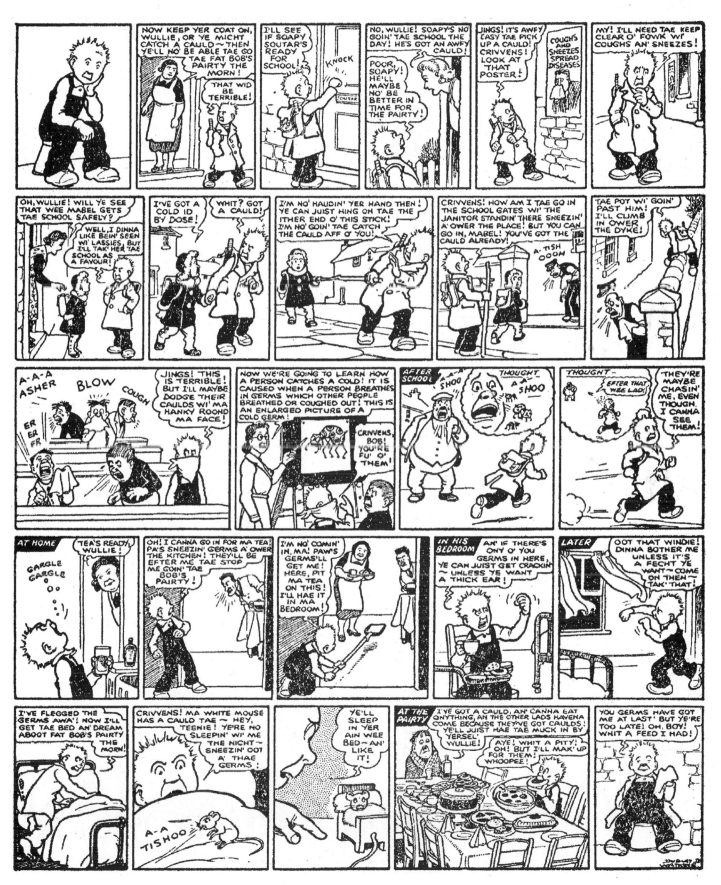

CHAPTER ANE: *A CLEAN GETAWAY*

On a bright morning, as the sun shone down on Auchenshoogle, Wee Harry and his best friend Jock strolled back to Oor Wullie's garden after a highly productive hour chasing a stick through a pile of leaves, both in full agreement that no stick had ever been more thoroughly chased, chewed and chucked about. Wee Harry and Jock were dogs, you see, so such work was common for them.

"Tomorrow we might find some mud tae roll aboot in," said Harry, planning ahead. He liked to think he was the brains of the pair.

"Aye," agreed Jock, who liked a good roll in the mud as much as the next dog. "But will Wullie no' be annoyed if ye get yer white fur a' covered in glaur?"

Harry barked a laugh. "Naw! Ye should hear the fuss he gets frae Ma when he comes hame wi' muddy boots, dusty dungarees, an' dirt behind his lugs."

"Harry, that laddie o' yours sounds like an honorary dug, richt enough."

Harry snuffled with pride. "Aye. It's no jist cats that land on their feet."

"Whit wis that aboot cats?" came a squeak from the timorous beastie sitting on the garden wall, who bared his teeth and tried to rear up to a great height. Unfortunately, since he was a mouse, that wasn't very high at all.

"Calm doon, Jeemie." Jeemie, or Wee Jeemie, as he is sometimes called, was Wullie's pet moose. "I jist meant that I landed on ma feet when I ended up wi' Wullie. An' there's nothin' I wouldnae dae for him." As he spoke, Harry's head stretched to the heavens. He knew there was never a more loyal dog. "Oh, mornin'."

That "mornin'" was meant for the man coming out through the gate carrying a ladder, who stepped aside to let the dogs enter Wullie's garden.

"I mean," continued Harry, "I'd guard that laddie frae ony danger. Invaders, robbers, burglars, postmen — I'd like tae see ane o' them gettin' past ma watchful eye." Harry smiled at his own bravery. "Wait a minute — whit's this fella comin' back for? Och, that's fine, it's jist Wullie's bucket he's takin' awa. Noo, as I wis sayin', nae thief nor burglar —"

"Burglar?" asked Jock. "The anes that use ladders tae get intae hooses an' carry aff valuables?"

"Aye. Noo dinnae interrupt —"

"Like thon fella wi' the ladder that's puttin' stuff in yon van?"

"Aye. Noo, as I wis sayin', naebody like that wid get past me. No' wi' the crown jewels, the Dona Lisa…"

"Or Oor Wullie's bucket!"

"Or Oor Wullie's — WHIT???"

Sure enough, the ladder man was loading a bucket into the back of the van.

"Burglar! Efter him!"

But there was a mammoth obstacle in their way.

"The cunning villain," groaned Jock. "He's closed the gate, an' we've only got wee legs. We cannae get ower it."

Harry was distraught! "An' Wullie will never get ower it if his bucket's stolen frae under oor noses an' we never lifted a finger — er — paw tae stop the crime!"

"Noo," cried Jeemie, "dinnae be hasty, Harry."

Harry was shocked by such disloyalty from Wullie's own pet moose. "Efter a' Wullie's done for you! Whit are ye, a moose or a moose?"

Stunned, Jeemie could only watch as Harry took a run at the gate, then skidded to a halt having eyed the towering barrier up close. "It's nae use. I'll need tae boost ye ower the top, Jock. Get yer hind leg on ma front paw… Ouch! Youb ob by dose! Oof! Noo, when I shove, you jump!"

"Gie it mair oomph, Harry!" shouted a shaky-legged Jock.

What Harry gave it was less 'oomph', and more 'OOYAH!' as a sudden pain shot up his tail, making him leap into the air, dunting Jock nose-first over the wall, so they both landed in a jumble of paws and fur on the other side.

There was no time to figure out what had nipped at his tail. They had to act fast as the ladder man was distracted, talking on his phone about, "a really big job". By another stroke of luck, the van's back door lay open, giving them their chance to foil the scheme by rescuing the bucket then and there!

With a scurry, a scamper, and a hop, the two dogs were in the back of the van.

"Grab the bucket," panted Harry urgently.

"Which ane?" replied Jock.

"Michty!" yelped Harry. "I've never seen sae many buckets. Big anes, wee anes, plastic anes an' steel anes." Then a thought struck him. "Ye ken whit this is, Jock? We've only gone an' infiltrated an international bucket rustlin' operation! Ye heard him talkin' aboot a big job! These must be aboot tae be smuggled oot the country an' sold tae the highest bidder."

"An' that's whit the ladder is for," replied Jock. "Tae get tae the high bids?"

"Naw, Sherlock Bones," squeaked a voice.

"A stowaway," grunted Harry, as Jeemie emerged from a tuft of fur on his back. "How did you get here?"

"Remember that sharp pain that got ye ower the wall?" He bared his front teeth. "That wis me."

"So ye bit ma tail tae mak' sure we stayed on the crook's tail?"

"Naw. I bit it because ye were bein' cheeky." Jeemie thrust his small paws on his hips. "Me, disloyal tae Oor Wullie? Ha! An' anither thing, hae ye never heard o' lookin' before ye leap? That goes for leapin' tae conclusions too. For if ye had looked, ye'd hae seen Wullie's bucket still sittin' whaur it aye sits!"

Jock and Harry squinted sheepishly out the van's doors and into Wullie's garden where said bucket was sitting soundly.

"But whit aboot a' these?" asked Harry. "An' the ladder?"

"Those buckets are for soapy water."

"Who's Soapy Water? I thoucht his name wis Soutar?"

"Naw, Jock. No' Wullie's pal. I mean water wi' soapy bubbles in it fir cleaning. An' the ladder's tae reach high windaes — whit wi' the lad bein' a windae cleaner."

Under his fur, Harry blushed. "But if he's no' a burglar, why did ye come tae help chase him?"

It was Jeemie's turn to blush. "Weel, when I bit ye an' ye jumped, I — um — forgot tae let go…"

CHAPTER TWA: *BOTANIC PANIC*

Before they could beat an embarrassed retreat, the doors slammed, the engine roared, and they were off! The buckets were rattling so loudly they could have barked and squeaked themselves hoarse without being heard.

When they peered out through the back windows, they saw none of the familiar streets and houses, only a long, wide road with more cars on it than they could count.

"Lads, I've a feelin' we're no' in Auchenshoogle onymair," said Harry.

Finally, the van slowed and stopped. "Aboot time too!" Jock scurried desperately to the door. "I jist hope there's a tree nearby!"

He was in luck. The first thing he saw — aside from the legs of the driver, who was too busy unloading his ladder to notice two dogs leap past with a mouse hanging on for dear life — was a vast, sprawling garden where people strolled or sat picnicking on the grass, all surrounded by trees. "Oh, whit a relief!"

Once they'd — er — attended to business, they noticed the great glass greenhouse in the centre of the garden. And just as the garden was much larger than the one at home, this was the biggest greenhouse they'd ever seen. It had a long, low, curved roof, and a massive glass dome in the centre.

"Michty!" marvelled Jock. "Imagine the size o' the flooers they must grow in there."

Harry shrugged. "I wis imagining the amount o' pocket money Wullie would be docked for ane careless kick o' his fitba near that."

"That must be the big job the ladder man meant," Jeemie sighed. "If he's here tae clean a' those windaes, it'll be days afore he's ready tae drive back."

"Days?" Harry paced in frantic circles, imagining poor Wullie getting more and more worried as time passed. "Och, naw! We hae tae dae somethin' noo!"

"Aye, like calm doon," groaned Jeemie, who was dizzy from Harry's racing around. "We need a plan. We dinnae even ken whaur we are!"

"There cannae be that many big roads jammed wi' traffic like the ane we drove doon," insisted Jock. "We'll easy find it, then jist follow it back."

"Hmmm…" muttered Harry, as they stood at the gates a few minutes later, gazing out at the large, busy roads. "Ye were sayin'?"

Jock ran over to the people gathered by traffic lights waiting to cross. "It has tae be ane o' these roads." And as the lights changed, they hurried across with the crowd, then tried to keep pace with the rapid feet as they marched along the pavement.

"These fowk seem tae ken whaur they're headed," Harry said confidently. "So we'll jist tag along." Then the direction of the pair of feet they were following suddenly changed, and they found themselves indoors where someone behind a window insisted that dogs weren't allowed onto the underground without leads. The owner of the feet didn't like this and argued that the animals weren't anything to do with him. A chase swiftly ensued, and in the confusion the two dogs with Jeemie in tow found themselves running towards, then under, a barrier, and down a lot of stairs, losing themselves among the feet of a crowd that stood looking expectantly at huge, round holes in the wall.

Jeemie's eyes boggled. "Look at the size o' thon mooseholes!"

"Ach! Ye dinnae get mice that big. Think how much cheese they'd get through!" said Jock.

But it wasn't giant mice that came squealing out of the tunnels. "Worms!" cried Harry.

"Ach, no' since the vet gave me thon tablets," protested Jock. Then he noticed the huge orange things that slid out of the tunnels. "Michty! They dinnae jist hae big greenhooses, they've got big gairden worms tae go wi' them. An' they're full o' people!"

And Jock was right as, within seconds, they were full of people, plus two dogs and a mouse as they got caught up in the rush and carried along inside the great orange beast, which rattled away into the tunnel again. But once they'd managed to clamber up onto the seats to look out at the darkness whizzing past, they had to admit it was surprisingly comfy inside these big worms.

But as more people got on, they were shooed off the seats to make room, and found themselves down among the feet again. Then, once those feet started moving at the next stop, they were swept out onto another platform and, like clockwork, the massive worm clattered off again.

"There's... PUFF... an awfy lot... PECH... o' stairs..." gasped Harry, as they climbed toward ground level again. Under another barrier they crept, and under the noses of the people behind the window who were handing out what must have been tickets to folk who were keen to go for a hurl on the orange beastie. Once out of sight round the corner, they stopped to catch their breaths.

"It's guid no' tae be on the move for a while," puffed Jock, not even noticing that they still were on the move, even though they were sitting still. The metal stairs beneath them were carrying them up toward daylight.

"If they had these in Auchenshoogle, PC Murdoch could dae his beat withoot liftin' his feet," grinned Harry.

Jock wasn't grinning, though. "Giant worms an' magic stairs? I'm hidin' till this is a' ower!" And the next thing Harry and Jeemie saw was Jock's stumpy black tail waggling as he nudged his way in among a pair of suitcases a couple was pulling hurriedly past. The couple was too busy checking their watches to notice their luggage had grown little legs, so Harry, with Jeemie safely on board, scurried in beside Jock. He just hoped that those cases were heading for a holiday close to home, and they weren't going to find themselves stranded somewhere thousands of miles from Auchenshoogle...

CHAPTER THREE: LO-COMMOTION ENGINE

There was a hairy moment a few minutes later when the luggage was carried across a steep gap and the lads had to jump over, but, once stowed away in among more bags and cases, the noise and movement around them was forgotten as they each dozed off. It was only when a loud growling started that they woke.

"Ye werenae dreamin' ye were a Rottweiler again?" Harry asked.

Jock pointed to his belly, as it let out another rumbling growl. "We've no' eaten in ages."

Just then, a man wheeled a trolley close to their hiding place. "Oor luck's in!" squeaked Jeemie, for the trolley was loaded with food.

"They'd surely no' miss ane wee sandwich," shrugged Jock, craning to sniff out the goodies. "Maybe a biscuit. An' a few sausage rolls..."

"Ony o' those cheesy crackers?" drooled Jeemie.

"I'll crackers the pair o' ye," snapped Harry, as Jock's wriggling tipped them all out of the luggage compartment and onto the floor.

"Hey!" shouted the trolley man.

"Scarper!" yelled Harry.

Running along the aisle while the countryside shot past outside the windows, Harry cried, "We're in another o' those worm things! At least we're above ground this time."

Jeemie popped up from the tuft of fur next to Harry's ear, and as he looked around a memory struck from the times Wullie had taken him with him on summer holidays. "Worm nothin'! It's a train!"

Harry paused, glancing up at the passengers looking down at him. "Oh, aye. A train. Weel, aye... I knew that a' along."

But he didn't pause for long, as there was a clatter of wheels, and the man with the food trolley insisted, "they dugs dinnae hae tickets!"

He tried to give chase, but the aisle was too narrow and his trolley was too wide for him to get past, so he had to trundle it ahead of him as he wobbled after the fugitive pets. And as he ran, he called out apologies to the passengers who'd wanted to buy sandwiches and cups of tea. It was a heavy trolley, and he puffed and panted in pursuit, but the dogs easily outran him along the length of the carriage. And that was even with stops to pick up all the snacks that flew their way from the hurtling trolley.

"Thank ye! Awfy kind," Harry said to the red-faced trolley man. Or at least he tried to say it — it's not easy to say much when you're hanging onto a packet of crisps, an apple, and a pork pie with your teeth.

And when the train slowed and stopped, Jeemie burrowed into Harry's fur, clinging on as the dogs leapt out, raced through more crowds, up a ramp, and into daylight again.

"It's good to be outside," said Jeemie, clinging onto a little packet of individual cheese biscuits, "and it's braw weather for a picnic."

CHAPTER FOWER: HAEIN' A CAPITAL TIME

Across the road there was a big green park — the ideal place to lie low, have a bite to eat, and make their plans. Then, fed and refreshed, they lazed in the shade of a bush. Peeping out, Harry said, "Ye see the big hoose on yon hill?"

If it was a house it was certainly bigger than Oor Wullie's — bigger even than the house and shed put together. It sat on a craggy clifftop, with turrets and chimneys, and flags flying overhead. It was so high above everything else they would surely be able to see their own houses from up there?

The problem was, being so low down themselves, it was easy to get lost among crowds, and everything seemed to be uphill, so they were soon panting again — even Jeemie, who had his work cut out hanging on as Harry dodged this way and that along busy, winding streets.

Jock suddenly came to a halt. "We can ask this laddie. Hey! You up there," he barked up at a small, grey terrier, who sat on top of a pillar.

"How did he get up there?" wondered Harry. "He'd hae tae be part cat."

Jeemie shuddered. "I hope the cat part's no' his mooth!"

"Shoosh! I'm tryin' tae ask for directions," grumbled Jock. "Hey, can ye see the way tae the big hoose frae bein' stuck up there?"

"Stuck up is richt," Harry muttered. "Look at him, no' even botherin' tae look doon his nose at us."

A little bus had pulled up, and the people piling off all pointed cameras and phones at the silent dog. A woman with a loud voice and an even louder tartan suit declared, "Here we have the famous Greyfriar's Bobby."

"Greyfriar's Snobby, mair like," Harry tutted. "Posin' for photies, an' no' helpin' his fellow dugs."

"Maybe he doesnae ken the way," shrugged Jeemie. "Ye get a lot o' tourists in these big places, I hear."

Jock was watching as the folk from the bus listened intently to the woman in tartan. "There's somebody wha sounds like she kens her way aboot. Quietly, lads..." And while the group were too busy snapping the dog on the pillar to notice two more dogs on the ground, they crept onto the bus and hid under a pile of coats on the back seat. They were safely cosied in when the passengers got back on board and the tartan lady announced, "Please fasten your seatbelts, as our whistle-stop tour of Scotland continues."

CHAPTER FIVE: *THON SINKIN' FEELIN'*

"We've been under this coat for ages," muttered Jock, "an' apart frae some sweets that… er… accidentally fell oot o' the pocket, I'm fed up o' bein' in the dark."

"I think we've stopped. I'll hae a wee peek." The bus was still, the passengers outside. But Harry's nose wasn't up against the window long before he ducked back under with a whimper.

"Michty, Harry! Ye've gone as white as… weel, ye're aye white. But ye're shakin' frae top tae tail."

"We're no' goin' oot there!"

"How no'?"

"I'll tell ye how no'! There's quicksand, that's how no'!"

Jeemie gulped. "Quicksand?"

"There were twa horses oot there, an' a' ye could see o' them were their heids stickin' up oot the groond!"

"We need tae help them," barked Jock, charging off the bus and towards the horses. It was only when he lifted his head up that he stopped. For he had to keep lifting it up, up, up a bit more, and still those great silvery grey heads towered higher and higher.

Seconds later he was back under the coat, muttering, "They looked big enough tae climb oot themselves. An' if it's up tae their necks, we'd be sunk wi'oot a trace in nae time at a'!"

"Maybe," said Jeemie, "we should jist stay cooried in here a wee while longer?"

And a wee while later, when the bus reached its next stop, Jeemie was talked into volunteering to check all was clear. A tiny nose peeped out. "I can smell salt," he sniffed. "An' fish?"

"Braw," yipped Jock. "We must be near Toni's chip shop!"

But there was no chip shop. The passengers snapped photos of boats, nets, and the wide open sea that spread out from a busy harbour, while the tartan lady spoke of picturesque villages and the hardy life of the fishermen.

"We could cadge a lift on ane o' the boats," said Jock, racing across the harbour, crying, "Ye dinnae happen tae go along Stoorie Burn?"

"Slow doon," yelped Harry, giving chase. But the sea spray had left the ground wet and slippery, and even as Jock stopped, Harry charged into him, and they all went skiting off the edge of the harbour.

"We'll be droont!" barked Jock. Only it wasn't the water they landed in. Though it was still wet, cold, and very slippery.

"We're in wi' today's catch! Let us oot o' here." They slithered and sank through the heap of fish more than they climbed, but eventually they flopped onto the deck and staggered across the gangplank.

"Am I glad tae be on solid ground again!" panted Jock.

"Dinnae bark too soon," whispered Jeemie, pointing to a pair of mean, green eyes that peered down at them from the harbour wall. "Talk aboot oot o' the fryin' pan…"

"Frying, ye sssay?" hissed the large ginger cat that glared hungrily at them. "I like my fish fried, but I'll take it however it'sss sserved."

Harry growled. "Dae we look like fish tae you?"

The cat's sharp claws gleamed. "It'sss no' what ye look like. But it'sss definitely what ye sssmell like. Eh, boysss and girlsss?"

More greedy eyes glared from every corner and shadow.

"We're naebody's fish supper," growled Harry, racing for cover with Jock in hot pursuit. Well, the pursuit may have been hot, but the hiding place they chose in the back of a big white truck wasn't hot at all. It was icy cold, with a very fishy smell. "We're fresh oot o' other places tae hide," moaned Harry.

"Fresh isss jist whit ye'll be when ye end up whaur you're headed," purred the grinning ginger cat, as the truck door closed. "Have an ice trip, boysss!"

CHAPTER SIX: LOCH AYE, THE NOO!

Blocks of ice and piles of fish aren't the most comfortable things to share a journey with. And it wasn't just the temperature that was growing frosty. "Whit I wouldnae give for a fur coat ower ma fur coat," chattered Jock.

"Ach, wheesht yer complainin'."

"Don't you tell Jock tae wheesht," grumbled Jeemie.

"Och, standin' up for him, are ye?" growled Harry. "Go an' use his fur as a blanket, then."

"Naw! It's jist that we could dae wi' some hot air in here, an' you've said Jock's full o' that!"

"Ye said WHIT?!" Jock bared his teeth. Though not for long, as they were chattering too much.

"Ach, I jist meant ye sometimes exaggerate."

"I've told ye a million times, I dinnae exaggerate!"

"Lads," Jeemie protested, "this is nae time tae fall oot!"

Which is exactly what they did do, when the van doors suddenly opened and they tumbled to the ground.

"Whit's this?" cried the startled driver. "The delivery form never said onythin' aboot dogfish."

"Aye, very finny," snapped Jock, as the three pals raced away from a carpark full of tour-buses and sightseers' cars, and down to the edge of the vast, deep loch stretching out invitingly ahead of them.

"It'll be cauld," warned Harry.

"No' as cauld as that van," cried Jeemie. "And we'll be rid o' the smell o' fish."

SPLASH, SPLOSH, and a tiny SPLISH, and they were in and out of the water again. "Sorry aboot oor wee misunderstandin', Jock," Harry muttered, as they stood dripping on the bank.

"Ach, it wis nothin', pal," grinned Jock. "Shake?"

And they did, sending water spraying everywhere as they shook themselves dry.

There was another, much louder SPLASH, and they turned in time to see a dark head on a long neck sinking into the depths.

"Oh, wow!" came a yell. "We've just got to get a photograph of that!"

Harry gazed across the rippling water, spying a dark shape lurking just beneath the surface. "I think ye missed it."

"Oh, how adorable! How cute!"

Jock shrugged. "Thon beastie didnae look cute tae... Here, are they takin' photies o' us?"

"They're so typically Scottish, the folks back home will go wild for these little fellas."

Wee Harry perked up. "Mak' sure ye get ma best side."

"Huh," muttered Jeemie. "An' you said that wee dug up that pole was a poser. Hmmm... weel, dinnae hog the camera. Let me gie them ma cheesiest grin."

But when he popped up, there were shrieks of 'rat', and quick as a flash the camera flashes ceased as the crowd raced back to a familiar tartan-clad lady who ushered them onto their bus.

"Och, that wis oor bus, too. We'll never catch it noo."

"Weel, at least they didnae catch me on camera," laughed a rumbling voice, as that darkly glistening head emerged from the water atop its long, powerful neck.

"I think we met a cousin o' yours," said Jock. "Big orange beastie livin' undergroond?"

"Some fowk'll believe onything," shrugged the creature. "But you saved ma photo ending up in the papers. No' that I mind tourists, noo. But when they get excited ye cannae swim in peace wi'oot bumpin' intae research submarines an' survey boats."

"That sounds enough tae gie onybody the hump," agreed Harry.

The creature gurgled a laugh. "Ye can say that again!" And as it swam away, the last they saw was a row of big, round humps before they sank out of sight under the loch.

CHAPTER SEVEN: STAGGERIN' ONWARDS

ours later, the three pals were trudging through long grass, hoping they were going in the right direction. They'd paddled across burns and streams, scrambled over rough stone walls, wandered through woods, and tramped up and down some of the biggest hills they'd ever seen. But still there was no sign of home.

As Harry stepped into the latest burn, he was sure he heard the hiss of steam from his overheated paws in the cool water.

"Maybe that coo kens the way," said Jock.

"Whit coo?"

"That ane, wi' the big horns on its heid. Here, why are you backin' awa?"

Harry was backing away because he knew that the cow wasn't a cow at all. And those weren't horns but antlers.

"I wouldnae go askin' that big ane for a pint o' milk," gulped Jeemie. "Or any o' his mates." For more of the majestic animals were striding over the hill to stare at them warily.

"Oh, dear," gulped Jock.

The largest beast snorted. "Wha are you callin' a deer, shorty? We're stags!"

Harry growled. "Shorty? You're the anes that look like ye should be on shortie tins!"

That did it. With a loud bellow the stags charged. And with an even louder yelp, two wee dogs and a mouse ran, rolled, tripped and tumbled as fast as they could through trees and tussocks, over walls and under bushes, until they found themselves hiding behind a little wooden building that looked like Wullie's shed but on stilts. And in the distance they heard the stags laughing to themselves.

It had grown dark, the temperature fell, and it wasn't long before they were creeping up a ramp and through a little hatch. Inside they found straw to bed down in. But Jock peered around nervously. "Somethin' moved ower there. And whit wis that rustlin'?"

Jeemie laughed. "It's no' a tattie bogle, so there's nae need tae be so chicken!"

A squawk from the dark made them jump. "And whit's wrang wi' being a chicken, eh?" clucked a stern voice. "Any more squawk like that and you can find somewhere else tae coop up for the night. Now settle doon, we chickens hae an early start tomorrow."

"Up at the crack o' dawn, eh?"

That ruffled a few feathers. "Please dinnae say C-R-A-C-K in front of the eggs."

"Sorry, ladies," soothed Harry, huddling into a warm pile of straw. "And we better get some sleep too, lads."

"Aye, it's been a busy day," yawned Jeemie. "Whit wi' a big stag do, then endin' up at a hen night!"

CHAPTER EIGHT: *THE ROAD AN' THE MILES*

When they came to a halt in the city itself, as the farmer unloaded her supplies, they slipped out and set off in search of clues about where to go next.

And then… "It's a miracle!"

"Whit is?" asked Jock, as Harry stood quivering.

"Ower there! It's… it's…"

"It's Oor Wullie," squealed Jeemie. "He's here!"

The spiky hair, dungarees and boots were unmistakable. And there was the peashooter that had knocked PC Murdoch's helmet flying many a time. And even though he was sitting on a low wall, even his bucket was there!

Tearing across, they panted, "It's us! How did ye ken whaur tae find us?" But the figure on the wall didn't move. "Are ye in a huff or somethin'? We didnae mean tae run awa, only there wis this burglar…"

But no matter how they jumped, barked and squeaked, Oor Wullie took no notice. Luckily, though, someone in the tall building across the road did notice, and he couldn't believe what he saw out of the window. Quickly dialling the phone on his desk, he spluttered, "Haud the front page on the missin' pets story, then get me Auchenshoogle polis station on the line… oh, an' ye'd better order some sausages, an' a wee bit o' cheese…"

Wee Harry, Jock and Jeemie were puzzled by this impostor who clearly was not the real Oor Wullie. For a start, Wullie never stayed that still or that quiet for that long. They were puzzled again by the nice folk who came out of the tall building with bowls of food and water and made a fuss over them. Not that they were complaining, mind.

And they certainly weren't complaining when the ground shook with the approach of two massive feet they'd know anywhere. Particularly as they were followed by two scuffed boots they knew even better. Two scuffed boots, a pair of dungarees, and a smiling face.

"It's Wullie!" cried Harry, looking between the silent figure on the wall and the beaming laddie who ran over to scoop them up in his arms. "The real ane!"

Jock looked over Wullie's shoulder at PC Murdoch. "We'll come quietly. Ach, wha am I kiddin'?" He barked happily and loudly.

The man who had first spotted them sighed, relieved. "The editor was frantic there'd be nae story for this week's Sunday's Post, whit wi' Wullie bein' sae worried aboot these scamps. Then they turn up right ootside oor offices? It's unbelievable!"

"But try tae believe it," winked Murdoch. "It helps mak' a happy endin'. And noo, you three gadaboots are gettin' a polis escort hame, whaur ye'll be sentenced tae a slap up feed an' bein' made a proper fuss o', I'd reckon."

Murdoch reckoned right. They came back to a welcome fit for heroes returning from a great adventure. Which they were. But as Wullie said that night, "Nae mair wanderin' aff seein' the sights for you."

"Nae danger," yawned Jeemie, curling up to sleep.

Wee Harry wagged his tail as he looked up into his best pal's smiling face and thought, "There's the ane sight I'm aye happy tae see."

And that's the whole story, straight from the horse's… well, straight from the dog's mouth. "An' every word o' it true," Wee Harry insists. "Efter a', would I tell ye a shaggy dog story?"

B right and early the next morning — well, early, but they weren't feeling so bright — the pals scurried from one pile of straw in the hen house to another in a crate in the back of the farmer's van. After Harry had told the mother hen all about their travels and how worried the folks back in Auchenshoogle would be, she'd hatched a plan… though they weren't allowed to say H-A-T-C-H-E-D in front of the eggs either.

"This is the day the farmer goes tae visit her sister. You've more chance of finding someone tae help you in the city. She always takes some fresh farm produce, an' she'll no' notice you if you keep your heads doon."

And when they lifted their heads again a few hours later, they looked out on a river so wide it needed two bridges and a big wooden boat with three tall masts. "We'll no' be doggy paddling across, then?"

THE END

Wullie gets his work ahead —

then he's aff tae kip in bed!

GETTIN' READY FOR CHRISTMAS

AH'M GETTING A'THING ORGANISED IN ADVANCE.

FIRST, I'LL HANG UP MY STOCKING.

AN' LEAVE OOT A GLASS O' MILK FOR SANTA AND A MINCE PIE FOR RUDOLPH.

I KEN FINE IT'S JUST PA THAT AYE EATS IT—BUT I DINNA WANT TO LET ON I KNEW ABOOT IT.

AH'M A SMART WRAPPER—AN' NO' THE SINGING KIND AFORE YE SAY IT!

NOW TAE PIT OOT MY PREZZIES TAE MA AN' PA UNDER THE TREE.

AN' SOMETHING FOR HARRY... I DINNA BOTHER WRAPPING IT NICELY...

WUFF?

...'COS HE AYE OPENS IT EARLY ANYWAY! HEH!

RRRIP!

ON WI' MA'S BEST TABLE CLOTH...

...AN' THE BEST KNIVES AN' FORKS.

IT WIDNAE BE CHRISTMAS WITHOOT THE CRACKERS!

I'VE SENT A' MY CHRISTMAS CARDS, TIDIED MY ROOM... AYE, THAT'S ABOUT IT.

I CAN GO TO BED NOW — I CAN HARDLY WAIT.

BUT IT'S ONLY THE 22ND, WULLIE— CHRISTMAS DAY ISNAE 'TIL WEDNESDAY!

SUN 22

I KEN THAT! IT'S JUST I CANNA TAK' ALL THE WAITING— AH'M STAYING IN BED FOR THREE DAYS. G'NIGHT.

WHIT A LADDIE.

CHRISTMAS MORN—

IT WIZ WORTH A' THE WAITING! MERRY CHRISTMAS, A'BODY!

KEN. H. HARRISON.

It's an awfy shock tae greet—

A first-foot wi' ower many feet!

So that's all folks! In their long eighty years, starting with their debut in the Fun Section of The Sunday Post, The Broons and Oor Wullie have proven with their animal magnetism that they are friends to a' creatures great an' small.

Whether it be creature features or animal magic, The Sunday Post strips are packed to the gills with timeless timorous beasties, some coos, cuddies and a few asses thrown in for good measure! Time and time again, we see capers with furry friends are never too far from oor favourite family and wee laddie — with man's best friend, specifically Wullie's best friend, Wee Harry sniffing out trouble in a strip of his very own. We hope you enjoyed oor very own ode tae a moose, dog, cat, donkey etcetera, etcetera — the list could go on till the coos come home!

GUID NIGHT, SLEEP TIGHT,
AN' DINNA LET THE BUGS BITE!
AN' DINNA MISS OOR WEE MITE
IN YER SUNDAY POST . . . A' RIGHT?